Usborne
1001
Things to spot
on Vacation
Sticker Book

Hazel Maskell
Illustrated and designed by Teri Gower

Additional design by Nelupa Hussain
Cover design by Stephen Moncrieff
Edited by Anna Milbourne

Contents

Things to spot

This book is all about going on vacation – anywhere from sandy beaches to snowy wonderlands and camping out under the stars. Each vacation scene is packed with exciting things to find and count. There are 1001 things to spot altogether.

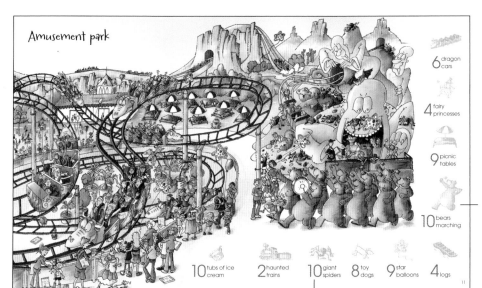

Amusement park

6 dragon cars

4 fairy princesses

9 picnic tables

10 bears marching

Each little faded picture shows you what to look for in the big picture.

10 tubs of ice cream

2 haunted trains

10 giant spiders

8 toy dogs

9 star balloons

4 logs

The number by each faded picture shows how many of that thing you need to find.

When you've found all of each thing, put a matching sticker on top of the faded picture. You'll find the stickers in the middle of the book.

Alex loves going on vacation, and she's heading off on a long trip all around the world. Can you spot her in each of the big pictures?

Plane trip

5 flowery shirts

8 eyemasks

2 straw hats

7 trays of food

9 cushions

6 cans of orange soda

10 sets of headphones

3 spotted suitcases

8 safety cards

9 puzzle books

Water park

3 lifeguards **4** waiters **9** ice cream sundaes **8** straw umbrellas **10** yellow armbands

6

 5 life rings

 2 pirate flags

 9 green swimming caps

 **7** toy dolphins

 **10** lounge chairs

Beach party

9 flower garlands

10 glasses of punch

8 corn cobs

9 slices of watermelon

3 yachts

7 steel drums

6 beach balls

1 ice cream cake

8 palm trees

10 paper
lanterns

Amusement park

10 tubs of ice cream

6 dragon coaster cars

4 fairy princesses

9 picnic tables

10 bears marching

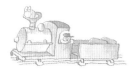
2 haunted trains

10 giant spiders

8 toy dogs

9 star balloons

4 logs

At the ranch

1 main lodge

6 foals

7 brown horses

8 backpacks

10 butterflies

9 water canteens **5** coyotes **8** jays **6** ranch cats **10** brown-and-white cows

Coral reef diving

8 yellow flippers

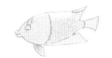

9 cleaner wrasse

8 clownfish

10 angelfish

4 blue sea stars

7 Moorish idols

10 snappers

1 zebra shark

2 octopuses

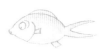

9 blue damselfish

Summer camp

5 log cabins

4 archery targets

9 climbing helmets

7 chipmunks

8 basketballs

Use these stickers on pages 4-5.

  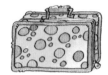  

Use these stickers on pages 6-7.

Use these stickers on pages 8-9.

Use these stickers on pages 10-11.

Use these stickers on pages 12-13.

Use these stickers on pages 14-15.

Use these stickers on pages 16-17.

Use these stickers on pages 18-19.

Use these stickers on pages 20-21.

Use these stickers on pages 22-23.

Use these stickers on pages 24-25.

Use these stickers on pages 26-27.

Use these stickers on pages 28-29.

Use these stickers on pages 30-31.

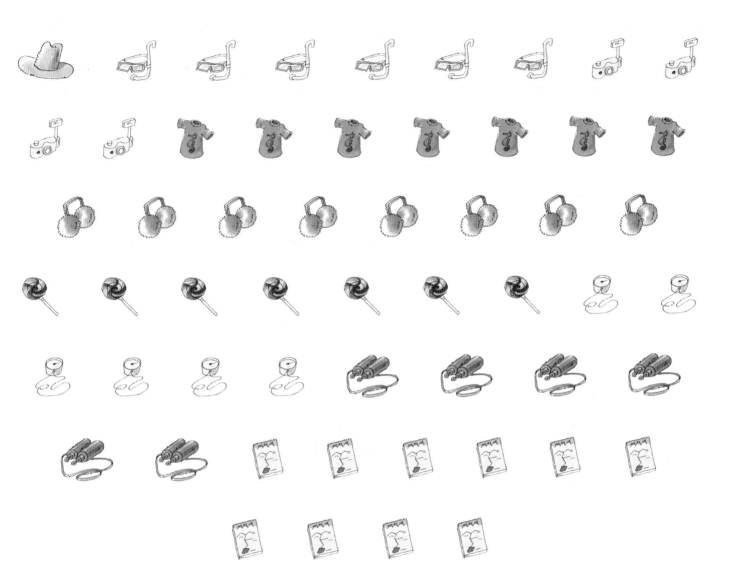

You could reward yourself by sticking one of these stickers on every
page when you've found all the things around the edges.

10 paddles

6 canoes

10 painted plates

9 ducks

3 trampolines

Whale watching tour

10 dolphins 7 portholes 6 seals 1 captain 9 gannets

 7 waterproof jackets

 8 cormorants

 1 whale tail

 7 seagulls

 6 fishing boats

On the ski slopes

9 snowboards

10 mugs of hot chocolate

3 snowmen

6 red poles

10 pink ski goggles

3 umbrellas

4 strings of lights

7 hungry birds

6 ski lift chairs

8 striped scarves

Carnival parade

7 tambourines

3 giant flowers

4 men on stilts

2 pink headdresses

5 juggling clowns

10 yellow pompoms

10 tall hats

7 elves

3 umbrellas

4 jesters

On safari

6 lion cubs

 **8** weaver birds' nests

 10 meerkats

 **7** hyenas

 **3** baby elephants

 9 antelope

 **4** termite mounds

 5 khaki hats

 **2** jeeps

25

Camping

5 green tents

7 chicken drumsticks

8 pancakes

10 plates of beans

5 drums

8 bats

5 striped sleeping bags

3 guitars

10 sticks of marshmallows

9 wooden mallets

27

Winter wonderland

8 snowshoes 5 huskies nd-
ats 9 reindeer

28

6 yellow sleds

5 tr

4 harnesses with bells

10 swans

Airport shop

Alex is at the airport shop, looking at all the things that are useful on different kinds of vacations. Look back through the book to spot them all, and add a sticker here for each thing you find.

6 boxes of pencils

6 books of ghost stories

6 packs of cards

10 hats with stars

9 blue-and-white caps

8 magazines

8 striped towels

9 cowboy hats

...ed in ...etri... ...ing or otherw... , witho... ...gdong, China. AE. First published in A...

6 white
diving masks

4 underwater
cameras

7 seahorse
T-shirts

8 sets of
earmuffs

7 swirly
lollipops

6 sets of
binoculars

10 guidebooks

6 compasses

Answers

Did you find all the things from the airport shop?
Here's where they all are:

6 sets of binoculars
On safari
(pages 24-25)

9 blue-and-white caps
Whale watching tour
(pages 18-19)

6 books of ghost stories
Camping
(pages 26-27)

8 magazines
Summer camp
(pages 16-17)

10 hats with stars
On the ski slopes
(pages 20-21)

8 striped towels
Water park
(pages 6-7)

9 cowboy hats
At the ranch
(pages 12-13)

6 boxes of pencils
Plane trip
(pages 4-5)

10 guidebooks
Amusement park
(pages 10-11)

6 white diving masks
Coral reef diving
(pages 14-15)

4 underwater cameras
Coral reef diving
(pages 14-15)

6 compasses
Camping
(pages 26-27)

8 sets of earmuffs
Winter wonderland
(pages 28-29)

7 seahorse T-shirts
Beach party
(pages 8-9)

6 packs of cards
Plane trip
(pages 4-5)

7 swirly lollipops
Carnival parade
(pages 22-23)

First published in 2014 by Usborne Publishing Ltd.,
Usborne House, 83-85 Saffron Hill, London EC1N 8RT, England. www.usborne.com